Woodland Secrets
Adventures in Ink
& Imagination

Publisher and Creative Director: Nick Wells
Senior Project Editor: Laura Bulbeck
Digital Manager: Chris Herbert
Art Director: Mike Spender

Special thanks to Frances Bodiam

Images in this book were crafted at the Flame Tree Studio, based on illustrations © copyright Black Moon, Maria Galybina, Gredi, Jake Jackson, Regina Jershova, Kotkoa, Olies, Mirrelley, Arthur Rackham (1867–1939) and Tashat.

This is a FLAME TREE book | First published 2016

FLAME TREE PUBLISHING
6 Melbray Mews, Fulham,
London SW6 3NS, United Kingdom

www.flametreepublishing.com

ISBN 978-1-78361-930-6

Manufactured in China

1 3 5 7 9 10 8 6 4 2

Words & Selection by Daisy Seal
Created by the Flame Tree Studio

FLAME TREE
PUBLISHING

The morning light plays across the meadows, with the poppies, and the cornflowers, sweet perfumes drifing

With me to the trees, butterflies dancing in my trail, I look ahead, and see creatures beckon, lifting

Into the leaves: are they elder folk, or birds? Soon I'm led to hidden pastures deep within, meandering streams

That murmur gently, that take me by the hand, and I turn to see the wood behind me, a tranquil dream.

Charming and delightful this beautiful new book offers many hours of calm and mindful pleasure, with so many illustrations for every mood, and a rhythm of easy, intermediate and more challenging pieces.

Woodland Secrets takes you by the hand, and introduces you to the meadows that sweep before a woodland copse, within which all manner of forest creatures play, and deeper still, a hidden garden of flowers, by a stream awaits, before you drift out, and look behind to the silhouettes of ancient trees, returning through fields to the rose gardens of home. If this is a dream, then it's pleasant indeed!

As with the previous book Secret Places, you can use a variety of pens: from gel and pencil, to pigment and crayon, from ballpoint and rollerball to highlighters, although it's best to avoid the heavy felt pens.

Each page is perforated near the spine of the book, so you can tear out and frame, perhaps even send them as a gift to a loved one. You'll have to make a choice about which design to make, if you want to tear it out, but with nearly 120 beguiling illustrations there's more than enough variety to help you make your selection.

Don't forget to sign your name at the bottom of the page, when you've finished each picture...

Woodland Secrets, inked by

Woodland Secrets, inked by

Woodland Secrets, inked by

Woodland Secrets, inked by

Woodland Secrets, inked by

Woodland Secrets, inked by

Woodland Secrets, inked by

Woodland Secrets, inked by

Woodland Secrets, inked by

Woodland Secrets, inked by

Woodland Secrets, inked by

Woodland Secrets, inked by

Woodland Secrets, inked by

Woodland Secrets, inked by

Woodland Secrets, inked by

Woodland Secrets, inked by

Woodland Secrets, inked by

Woodland Secrets, inked by

Woodland Secrets, inked by

Woodland Secrets, inked by

Woodland Secrets, inked by

Woodland Secrets, inked by

Woodland Secrets, inked by

Woodland Secrets, inked by

Woodland Secrets, inked by

Woodland Secrets, inked by

Woodland Secrets, inked by

Woodland Secrets, inked by

Woodland Secrets, inked by

Woodland Secrets, inked by

Woodland Secrets, inked by

Woodland Secrets, inked by

Woodland Secrets, inked by

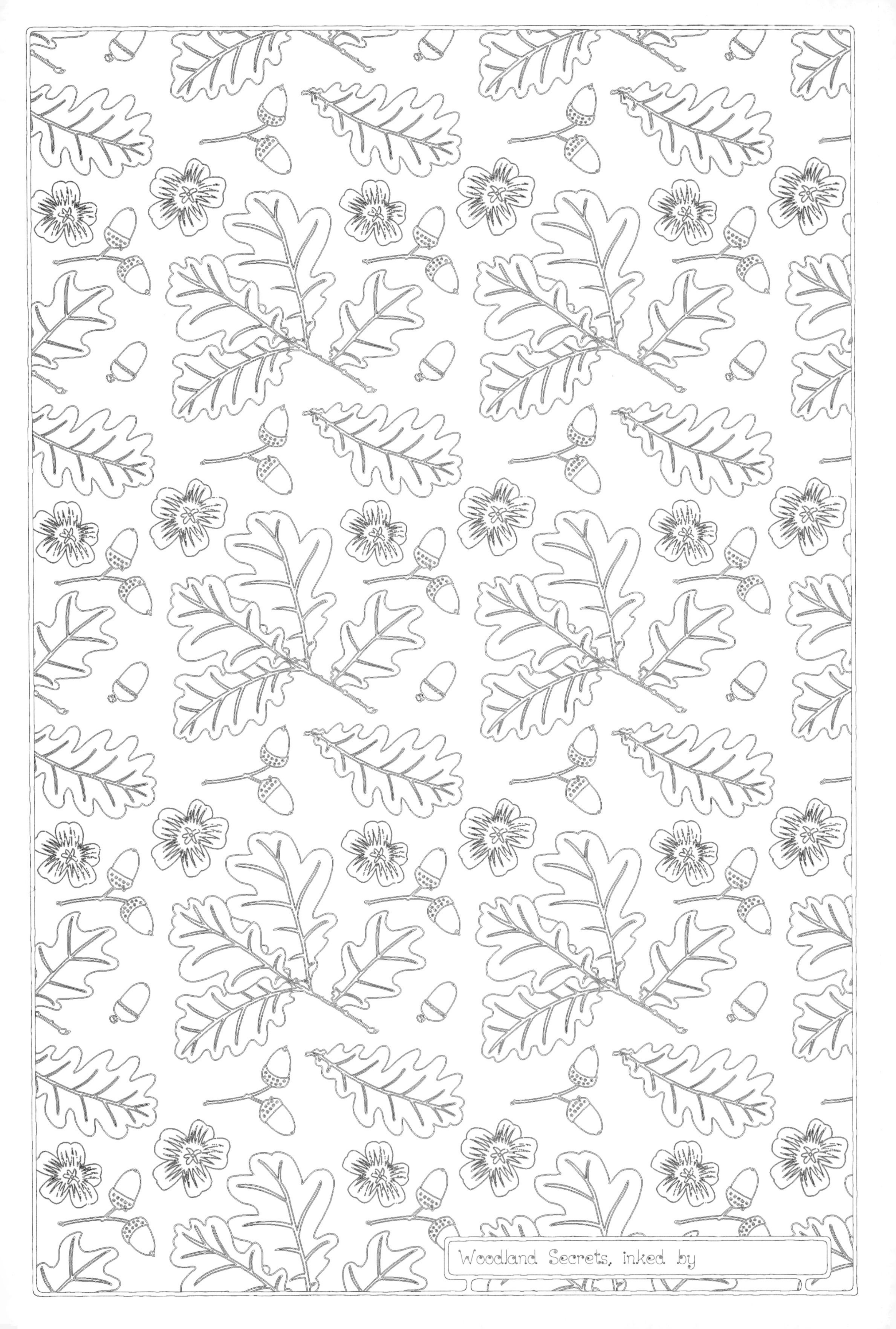
Woodland Secrets, inked by

Woodland Secrets, inked by

Woodland Secrets, inked by

Woodland Secrets, inked by

Woodland Secrets, inked by

Woodland Secrets, inked by

Woodland Secrets, inked by

Woodland Secrets, inked by

Woodland Secrets, inked by

Woodland Secrets, inked by

Woodland Secrets, inked by

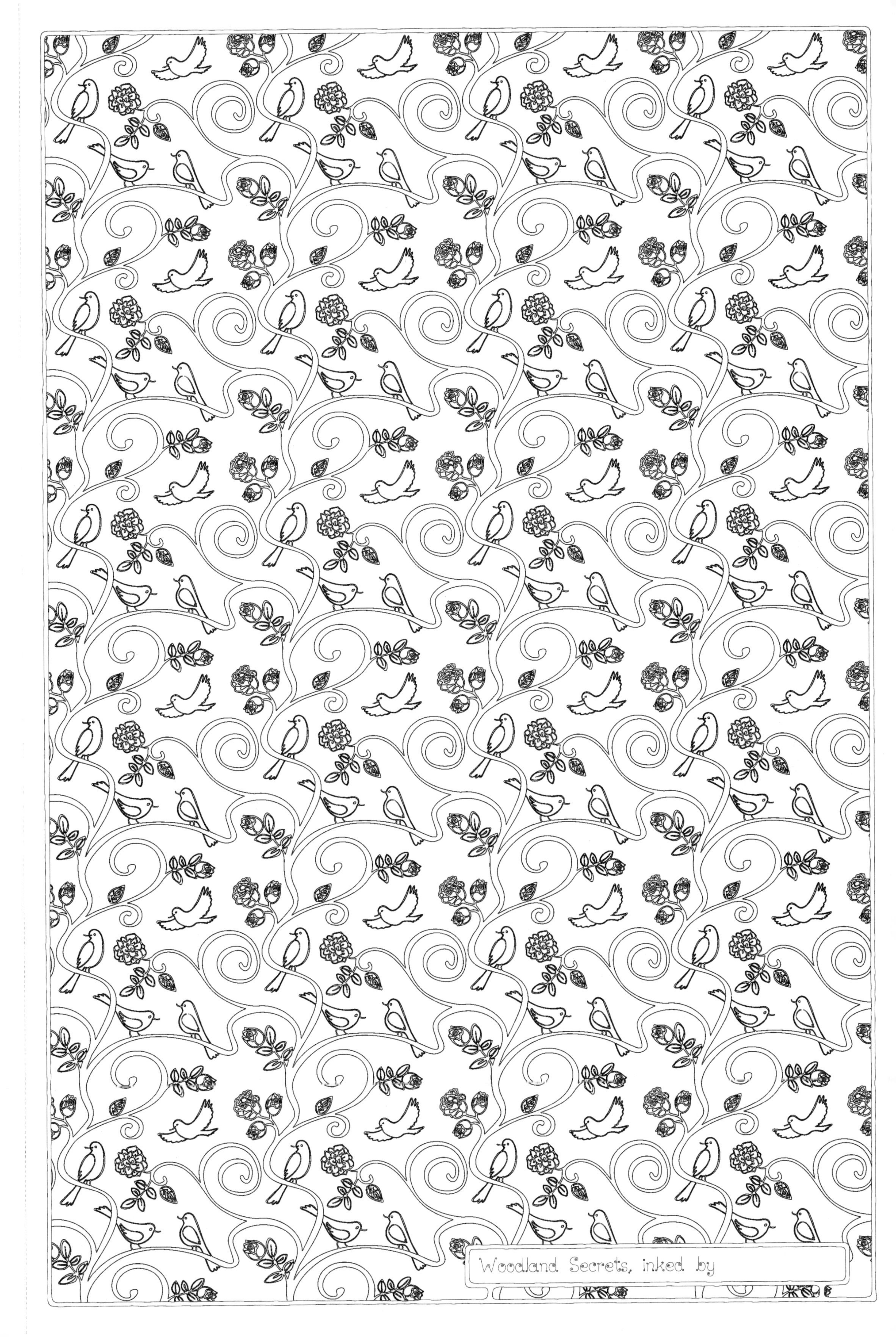
Woodland Secrets, inked by

Woodland Secrets, inked by

Woodland Secrets, inked by

Woodland Secrets, inked by

Woodland Secrets, inked by

Woodland Secrets, inked by

Woodland Secrets, inked by

Woodland Secrets, inked by

Woodland Secrets, inked by

Woodland Secrets, inked by

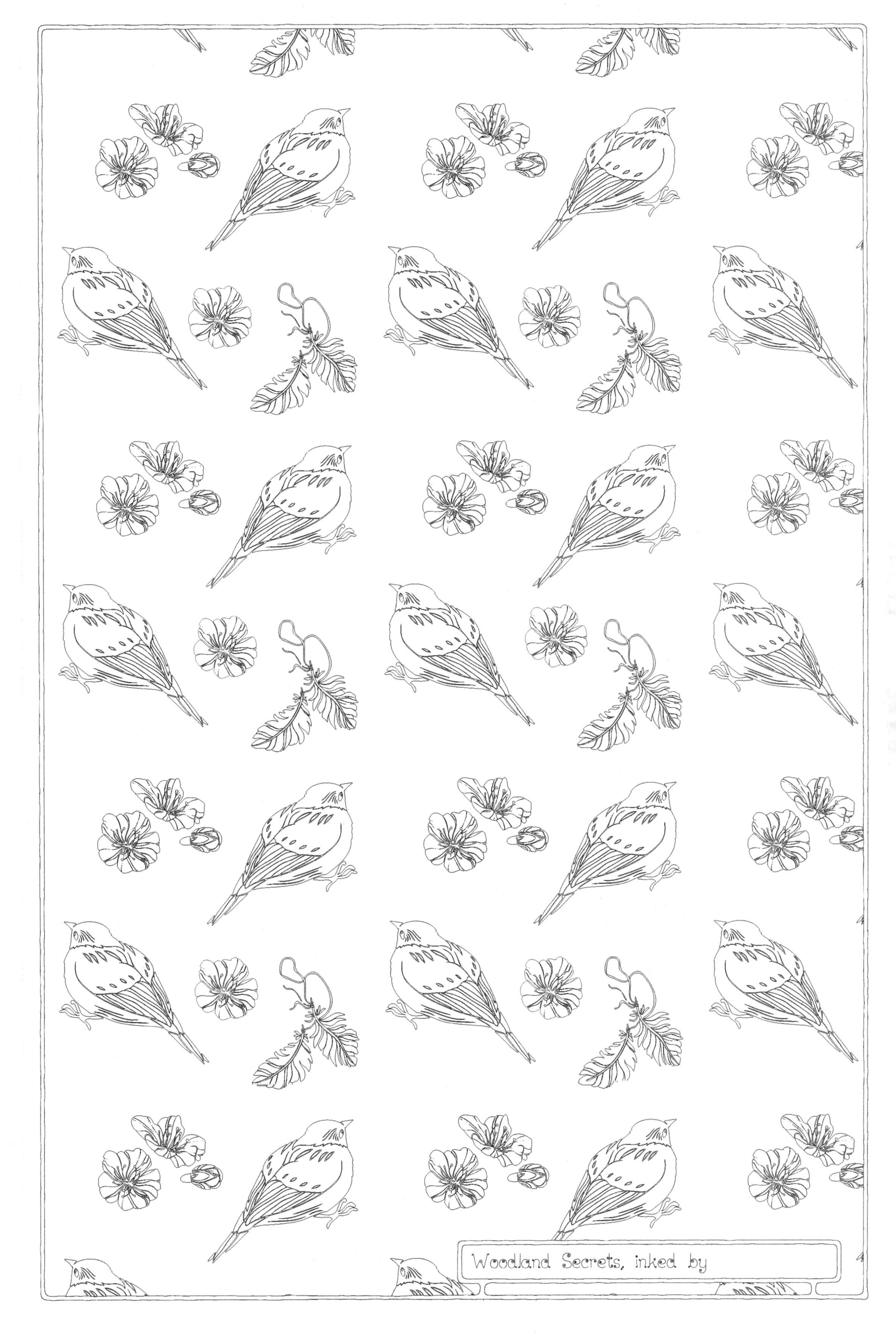
Woodland Secrets, inked by

Woodland Secrets, inked by

Woodland Secrets, inked by

Woodland Secrets, inked by

Woodland Secrets, inked by

Woodland Secrets, inked by

Woodland Secrets, inked by

Woodland Secrets, inked by

Woodland Secrets, inked by

Woodland Secrets, inked by

Woodland Secrets, inked by

Woodland Secrets, inked by

Woodland Secrets, inked by

Woodland Secrets, inked by

Woodland Secrets, inked by

Woodland Secrets, inked by

Woodland Secrets, inked by

Woodland Secrets, inked by

Woodland Secrets, inked by

Woodland Secrets, inked by

Woodland Secrets, inked by

Woodland Secrets, inked by

Woodland Secrets, inked by

Woodland Secrets, inked by

Woodland Secrets, inked by

Woodland Secrets, inked by

Woodland Secrets, inked by

Woodland Secrets, inked by

Woodland Secrets, inked by

Woodland Secrets, inked by

Woodland Secrets, inked by

Woodland Secrets, inked by

Woodland Secrets, inked by

Woodland Secrets, inked by

Woodland Secrets, inked by

Woodland Secrets, inked by

Woodland Secrets, inked by

Woodland Secrets, inked by

Woodland Secrets, inked by

Woodland Secrets, inked by

Woodland Secrets, inked by

Woodland Secrets, inked by

Woodland Secrets, inked by

Woodland Secrets, inked by

Woodland Secrets, inked by

Woodland Secrets, inked by

Woodland Secrets, inked by

Woodland Secrets, inked by

Woodland Secrets, inked by

Woodland Secrets, inked by

Woodland Secrets, inked by

Woodland Secrets, inked by

Woodland Secrets, inked by

Woodland Secrets, inked by

Woodland Secrets, inked by

Woodland Secrets, inked by

Woodland Secrets, inked by

Woodland Secrets, inked by

Woodland Secrets, inked by

Woodland Secrets, inked by

Woodland Secrets, inked by

Woodland Secrets, inked by

Woodland Secrets, inked by

Woodland Secrets, inked by

Woodland Secrets, inked by

Woodland Secrets, inked by

Woodland Secrets, inked by

Woodland Secrets, inked by

Woodland Secrets, inked by

Visual Arts

FLAME TREE PUBLISHING
flametreepublishing.com

From **How to Draw Manga** to **Tattoo Art**, **Alphonse Mucha** to **Drawing Basics**, we publish a range of fine and practical books, calendars and journals for artists and art enthusiasts.

If you enjoyed this book, please sign up for updates, information and offers on further titles on the visual arts at **blog.flametreepublishing.com/art-of-fine-gifts/**

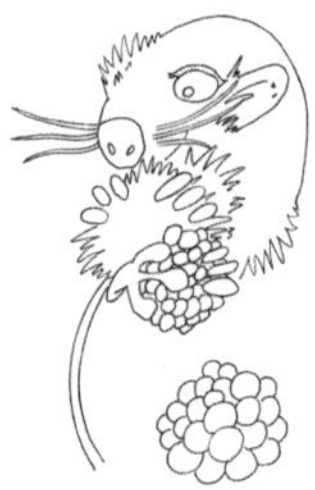